DEAR LORD ...
THE
RAMBLING PRAYERS OF
TERRY U. TYCHUS

by

Jeff Grist

MOORLEY'S Print & Publishing

British Library Cataloguing in Publication Data.
A catalogue record for this book is available
from the British Library.

ISBN 0 86071 498 5

MOORLEY'S Print & Publishing
23 Park Rd., Ilkeston, Derbys DE7 5DA
Tel/Fax: (0115) 932 0643

CONTENTS

About Terry

Allow me to tell you why I chose Terry U. Tychus as the character. When I first started writing these monologues, I needed a name that best described the type of character I wanted to convey, and of course, he had to have a Bible connection. As I read the book of Acts, I came across an account of Paul the Apostle preaching to one of his churches at Troas where he spoke all through the night. There was a young man sitting in the window listening, and at some point he fell asleep, lost his balance and plummeted to his death outside (Acts 20:9). Thankfully, Paul brought him back to life. His name was Eutychus, and I'm sure that he learned from his mistake. Terry is someone who learned from his mistakes, and so I incorporated U. Tychus into his name.

Jeff Grist

DEAR LORD...
THE GREAT COMMISSION

Dear Lord,

When you told us to go and spread the good news to all the nations, did you know of the problems different cultures coming together would bring? I mean, since our church's last evangelistic rally down on the pavilion, we have been joined by the Fosters, a family from New Zealand, which as you know, Lord, causes embarrassment during the international rugby season, (surely there's a commandment against smugness!) and the Hernandez' from Madrid! And I have grave doubts as to the wisdom of picking Jose' Hernandez to help catch members of our congregation at alter calls when they plop. (You don't mind me calling it "Plopping", Lord, only it seems that's what people do! They go, "ooh plop!" Apart from Mrs. Waters, that is. I wish she would lose weight. I mean, I know that I'm no cat-walk model but at least when I go swimming, I pose no danger to shipping! The last time I'd been given the "privilege" of catching people, I was allocated to Mrs. Waters. [My so-called colleagues aren't stupid.] She is not a plopper; more a thudder! And she had me pinned to the platform floor for quarter of an hour! Nobody knew I was there until she got up and I requested prayer... from where I lay!) But back to Jose'! You see Lord, my reason for doubt is this. When you go forward for prayer and you feel the Spirit set your heart on fire, and you start to plop backwards, the last thing you want to hear is a Spanish voice yell "Ole!!" Faith disappears and in walks fear! Most disconcerting! Thankfully he hasn't dropped anyone yet but watch him, Lord!

This causes me to consider carefully who I want to bring into the church, but I also know that's not how you want it to be! It is a place for all! That's why I'm asking you to save Simon at work! If ever a guy needs saving, it's him! I mean, did you hear what he called me yesterday? I know my ears stick out slightly but how he can call me "wing-nut" I don't know! Imagine asking me if my head spins around in the wind! Cheek! That guy's got an attitude problem! I'd love it if he found you, Lord! Then he'd stop giving me hassle! The trouble is that I can't stand the man! If he ever came to church and went forward for prayer, I'd put him right behind Mrs. Waters and wait for the crunch! How could you love him, Lord? He's just a pain! Mind you, sometimes I wonder how you could love me! And I suppose that's why I must rise above our differences. I shouldn't retaliate and be like him, but show him grace and forgiveness, and be like you! Yes, Lord, I will try to show him your example.

Thank you for listening to me!

DEAR LORD...
THE LEGEND OF THE SNAREDRAGON

Dear Lord,
    Life would be perfect if it wasn't for other people! I'm sure you know what I mean! They're nothing but trouble! Most of my problems are caused by other people! I'll explain.

    Two weeks ago, it was my daughter's birthday and we had a party. Nothing lavish Lord, you know! Stuff the kids with McDonald's beefburgers and french fries (that's chips, Lord!) a strawberry milkshake and a doughnut, half an hour in the bouncy castle, ten minutes to mop up the sick, birthday cake, candles, party bags, explain to Mrs. Jones why Robbie's got a blackeye, get home, sorted! Then, a quick shifty at the prezzies! Mostly harmless; Barbie's self pregnancy test kit, My Little Pony abattoir complete with apron, Jurassic Park disembowelling dinosaur, the usual "toys!!" Then I saw the book, "The Legend of the Snaredragon!" A lively tome emblazoned with a large, colourful picture of a purple dragon, for ages eight and over. This gift of dubious nature bestowed on my daughter by my sister and brother-in-law caused two reactions. Great delight in my eldest, and alarm bells in me! "A grown-up book!" she exclaimed. She's "in" to grown-up things at the moment, Lord! You know, ear-rings, clothes, Spice Girls! (insert latest teen group) I blame the school! It was a huge shock to her and a small sadness to us when she went to the autumn school fancy dress party made up as a cat, only to find out that fancy dress was "un-cool" and she was alone in her desire to remain a child! But soon after that, the Mothercare cassette of nursery rhymes was history! Out with Fisher price and bibbed dresses, in with Hot Hits 25 and fashion! And all this by the age of eight!

    And so the unadulterated delight caused by the arrival of "The Legend of the Snaredragon!" shouldn't have surprised me! But it did!

    Well Lord, considering that all my daughter knew about dragons in the past was pretty innocent, (you know, Pete's dragon and Puff!) I thought it best not to over-react! Indeed, I remember the time not so long ago when I enjoyed the odd science fantasy book or three without any real bother.

But, as you'll recall Lord, insidious things started to creep in and I was soon consulting my pastor as to my difficulties. A wise man (and I pray that you will continue to bless him and his family), he didn't ban me from reading them altogether, as then there was the danger that I would be acting from a man-led suggestion instead of spirit-led guidance. Alternatively, he suggested that I regularly read more wholesome material pertaining to your goodness, Lord! Feeding on God's words and works, he called it! And then I could enjoy some "junk food" now and again, but not all the time! (It was a bit like eating nourishing food mostly, but still enjoying a burger and fries at McDonalds on occasions!) And following his advice, I developed more of an appetite for the wholesome food but less and less for the junk, to the place where I rarely read them nowadays! They just seem to have lost their appeal! And so I felt that I didn't want to create a problem for my daughter that wasn't there! Now, she happily reads "The Legend of the Snaredragon!" along with her biblical tales, and Spice Girls Annual! (But if more dragon books start to appear, I'll re-evaluate the situation. Until then, shalom!)

Now Lord, another problem arose last Sunday. As you know, we only allow our children to take one book each to church to keep them amused when they don't feel like getting involved in the praise and worship. My son was suitably armed with "Thomas the Tank Engine!" but my daughter wanted "The Legend of the Snaredragon!" Immediately, pictures sprang to mind of the reaction this would bring when certain members of the congregation saw the sort of literature I was allowing my daughter to read. To Eric Bristow, a lovely man but a tad over-zealous for my tastes, the sight of a minor reading this material in church of all places would be tantamount to sacrificing virgins in the baptismal pool! So how would I explain to an eight year old that it was okay to read it at home but not at church? Kids can see hypocrisy a mile off! Hypocrisy to them looks like a morris dancer with a megaphone and a great sign on their head bearing the word "Hypocrisy" written in big, red letters!

Well, thank you Lord that you came to my rescue! As the apostle Paul said, "Everything is permissible but not everything is beneficial!" And just because we felt okay about the book (this time!) didn't mean that the other children would! I explained that their mummies and daddies might not like dragon books and it would not be good to encourage the other children to sin against their parents and you! Incredibly, she accepted this and promptly replaced "The Legend of the Snaredragon!" with "The Ugly Scarecrow" by Enid Blyton, and we left for church!

I suppose I wouldn't have had this problem if my sister hadn't given this book, but on reflection, I think it may have made us all a bit wiser! And it certainly helped my daughter to be mindful of your will and more thoughtful to others! So, other people do cause problems but that's not necessarily bad! It jolts us out of our complacency, and for that,

Thank you, Lord!

DEAR LORD...
AUTOSTEREOGRAMS

Dear Lord,

Sight is a wonderful sense, but if it's not used properly, it's useless! Last Christmas I visited my mother. (Not that I only visit her at Christmas Lord, though to listen to her, you'd think that was the case. No sooner am I saying goodbye than she's complaining that she never sees me!) I do try to see her often but it's not something that falls in my list of "Top ten things I want to do!" (It's probably laying around fifteenth!) The conversation is very one-sided. First I hear all about Aunty Sheila and the problems she's having with her wayward son! Then I get the ins and outs of my grandmother's lumbago. This is followed by a detailed account of her friend Sonya's latest love affair! By the time we get around to Mum's plans for her fifth foreign holiday this year, my mind has gone walkies and is now lolling about amongst the lush, green grasses of dis-interest! And the more often I visit, the quicker the journey to dis-interest! But, to be fair, since Dad died she's done very well and has kept busy, either planning holidays, or taking holidays! But last Christmas was different! As I sat there calling my mind to heel (and wondering where it's gone and whether I'd have to bath it afterwards!), Mum appeared carrying what I would describe as three colourful plastic place mats. She handed them to me saying that they were the latest craze! "What? Plastic place mats?" I thought. But she went on to explain that they were called "Auto-stereograms" and that the lots of colourful little dots printed on them held a secret 3-D picture. Well Lord, they just seemed like colourful dots to me! She sat me down and told me to stare at the picture and wait for something to happen. So, I stared and stared and sure enough, something did happen! I got a headache! She insisted that both she and my sister had seen pictures in them. Well Lord, I naturally presumed some demonic force at work here which was deceiving them. (You may recall that I prayed there and then!) That was why I couldn't see the pictures! I am covered by the Blood of the Lamb, and not so easily susceptible to demonic deception! Well, what a fool! In my ignorance, I was deceiving myself! Mum was determined not to give up on me and put me by a lamp so that the light was shining on my face and could be seen reflected in the plastic. She told me to stare and focus on my reflection! I pitied her as I looked, entirely unconvinced, hoping that you would show her the error of her ways. Suddenly, the edges of the picture sank back - and I saw a tyrannosaurus rex snarling back at me in 3-D!! Well Lord, it blew my mind! Mum stood over me triumphantly! (A pose I was to develop later.) It was true! I could look around this new picture and saw not only the T-rex, but also a Brontosaurus, a Stegosaurus, a "D'yah think 'e saurus", and in the air, a pterodactyl! It was quite amazing! This random blur of dots now held new wonders that I hadn't seen before! Then I blinked - and the picture was gone. So, I re-focussed my eyes and there it was again! Of course, once I'd done one I wanted to do them all! Mum gave me another and within seconds I was looking at a heart amongst some roses! Now I knew how to do it, it was simple. My wife held the third picture and sighed, saying she couldn't see a thing! Poor love! She was staring at the blank side on the back! I turned it around and soon she was whooping in delight at the revelations. Well Lord, I wanted some of these marvellous pictures to share, and in due course I was the owner of a book of them!

After wowing my colleagues in work with them (all, that is, except Simon), I ventured to take it to housegroup. What a mixed response! Eric Bristow was immediately suspicious, taking a similar stance to my first thoughts, and warned us not to dabble in the occult! I assured him that this wasn't the demonic but was accused of being deceived and I should take heed from an "elder who knew better!" Mrs. Waters thought that I'd called it "Auto-suggestion", and went on to say that she'd heard years ago that they used to flash subliminal messages up on the cinema screens, but so quickly that only your subconscious mind would see it, process the suggestion and turn you into an axe-wielding maniac! I did suppress the urge to ask her whether she had seen this at first hand! After all, she would make quite a formidable axe-wielding maniac!

Needless to say, neither she nor Eric would look. But my old mate Tony looked. I like Tony, Lord. We get on so well and have the same interests and sense of humour. He is a friend and a confidant, and a very reliable avenue of relief when things get a bit heavy at housegroup, like when Neil and Pat, the housegroup leaders, thought I was watching too much junk on T.V. Tony rescued me, though without excusing me, by mentioning the love of "Eastenders" and "Neighbours" that Pat holds. After that, grace returned! A good lad, Tony. But he also enjoys teasing the members of the housegroup. He would have said that he could see a picture in the auto-stereogram even if he couldn't, just to annoy the others. But thankfully, he did see the images. This aroused more interest and soon, one by one, they all looked, and were rewarded! All, that is, except Eric! He was adamant, and despite Neil's attempts to calm him down, he insisted that he was going to report the whole evening to Pastor Parcel! Poor Neil!!

But, do you know Lord, during the row, I caught a glimpse of what Jesus must have faced from the Jews. They had it fixed in their minds that he was a fake, a fraud, and a blasphemer, deserving of death, and nothing He could do would change their minds. As it says in the book of Romans when Paul quotes Deuteronomy and Isaiah,
"God gave them a spirit of stupor. Eyes so they could not see, and ears so they could not hear!" They could see Jesus, but their eyes, mind and heart were incapable of being re-focussed to see who He really was!

I thank you Lord that you are a God of fresh revelation. Your steadfast love never ceases and your mercies are new every morning! And I pray that every day, you will help us to re-focus our lives to see your will in every situation, and to see that a blurred and seemingly irrational circumstance can hold a deeper significance, if only we learn to see what you see!

Praise you, Lord!!

DEAR LORD...
TOLERANCE

Dear Lord,

What is the matter with the youth of today? I know I'm talking like I swore I never would when I was a teenager, but surely my generation weren't this bad! Youth culture is so foreign to me! I don't understand their music, if you can call that repetitive thumping and moronic chanting "music"! And I was never one for fashion but at least I could stretch to a bit more than a camouflaged flak-jacket and a bobble-less bobble hat! And that's just the girls! And when you talk to them, the way they look at you makes you think you've just landed from Mars!! They think they know it all. I've lost count of the times that a young lad or lass has crossed the road in front of my approaching vehicle. And when they do condescend to glance in my direction, do they regard self preservation a priority and hurry across? No!! They stop and stare at you, annoyed that you had the gall to break their train of thought, and seem to challenge your right to be where they are! Sometimes it takes all my strength not to reinforce my right of way with the ton and a half of growling metal that I'm sitting in!

Also Lord, their television programmes are mystifying! I grew up with Thunderbirds and Captain Scarlet (the first time round!), Joe 90, Fireball XL5, Lost in Space, etc. And there was a time when I knew at least one band on "Top of the Pops!" But not now! Now, they have "Def 2" and "The Word"! I mean Lord, I know we had Monty Python which we mainly didn't under stand but laughed at it anyway, and at least it wasn't offensive, nor directed at anyone. But nowadays... I'd better stop, Lord, or I'll be moaning all day!

I suppose it's because I'm getting older, and it's a different lifestyle now! Unfortunately, it's all computer games and drugs!

The only computer games we had was that tennis game or Space Invaders, and I was rubbish at them both! But now, who on earth is Zool? And as for drugs, the nearest I got to a rush was when I swallowed one of my gran's Do-Do decongestant tablets! Boy, was I high! I thought I could see cockroaches coming out of the walls! But really there were cockroaches coming out of the walls! Gran's house was very old!

Then I heard about the latest craze, Magic Mushrooms! But I could never understand how anyone could smoke a mushroom, even a magic one! I mean, how would you get it to light? I do accept that the culture today is very different to when I grew up. Being a parent makes you only too aware of the dangers that are present in today's society. When I was young, I would tell my mum where I was going, when I'd be back, and off I'd go down the brook, or building dens in the orchard! We used to build some great dens, Lord! There was me, Phil "Strangely" Brown, Robert "Me First" Harris, and Nigel "Limpy" Rees. (We called him "Limpy" because he had a deformed leg which caused him to limp! Kids can be cruel and I suppose we were no exception. He didn't mind, as I remember!) We were called "The cat skull gang" purely because Me First Harris found a cat skull in a clearing where our latest den was to be! We had lots of dens because "The Dogs' Paw Gang" kept raiding ours to make theirs! (We called them "The Dogs' Pooh Gang".) There was intense rivalry between us, especially at Guy Fawkes night. We'd steal wood from their bonfire and they'd steal from ours! So, we used to hide Strangely Brown inside the bonfire to give us warning. But one day, the Dogs' Pooh Gang changed tactics. Instead of stealing wood, they set the bonfire alight! We were so scared! Strangely Brown was in there! We yelled to our parents who called the fire brigade as well as setting up bucket chains to throw water on the flames. But by the time the fire was doused, there wasn't much left! How we cried and cried! We'd never confronted death before! Thankfully, we didn't have to this time. Strangely Brown appeared behind us asking what had happened to the bonfire!

Apparently, he'd got bored sitting amongst the wood and so went home to watch Joe 90. Hallelujah for Joe 90! I'm not sure that he would have gone in to watch "The Word"! It was a close call Lord, but praise you that all was well. Strangely Brown is a fireman now! Isn't that strange!

Apart from those incidents, life as a child was free and easy. But I accept that things are different. I mean, you only have to look at the news to see that it's dangerous to let your kids out of your sight for too long! There are more cars on the road, and more cases of child abductions and abuse. To amuse your child nowadays costs! And if you can't afford it, you amuse them at home with T.V. and computer games. Imaginations are limited leading to boredom, and quick fixes to relieve the tedium! Maybe this explains today's youth, Lord, I don't know! You still love them!

But I was walking to work this morning, minding my own business, when I saw a young lad walking towards me on the same side of the pavement. We got closer! I wasn't going to move! Closer still! Neither was he! What do I do? In my mind, I thought, "Shift, Kid!" But he was staying on the same side. "The youth of today have no respect or manners!" I thought. We got closer and closer! Then, he gave me one of those "Martian" looks! This should have made me more determined to stay on my side. But I decided to step to the right, and we passed without so much as a grunt! And now I think about it, is this the difference between Tolerance and Fanaticism? If I'd been fanatical about my position and continued to treat others as infidels, then I would have pounded the lad to the ground and walked over him! But instead, by a temporary change of position, but not changing direction, I was able to continue my walk without unnecessary confrontation. And I feel this is how you would like me to live Lord! Living your life style, travelling in your direction, but being tolerant and understanding to others so that we can all live together!

Amen!!

DEAR LORD...
LOVE

Dear Lord,

Some things in life are funny! Like the time Pastor Parcel was booked to preach to an outreach conference at the local recreation centre. But he got his dates wrong! He ended up delivering a sermon about "The Valley of the dry bones" to the Middleton dog show!! (Talk about a shaggy dog story!) Still, it was very popular with the canine members of the congregation! (Oh, have you heard the one about dyslexic agnostic philosopher who wondered, "Is there a Dog?" You probably have!)

And the time when Tudor Toffee only half caught Walter Wallcarpet when he "plopped", and inadvertently directed his head into one of the balcony pillars, resulting in "a loud wailing and a gnashing of teeth," plus Walter laying there a bit longer than usual! I know we're not to laugh at other people's misfortunes, Lord, but that was funny!!

But there are some things that are not funny, no matter how you try to "jolly them up!!" I was watching T.V. last night and this sitcom started. Basically, the story was about two couples; the wife of couple A was trying to commit an adulterous act with the husband of couple B, while the husband of couple A got drunk while he went through the agony of realisation that his wife was "playing away from home" to put it in the footballers' vernacular. In other words, she was off with another man! And what I don't understand Lord, is that it was a sad and tragic scene and the studio audience was in stitches with laughter! I couldn't see the joke, and as you know Lord, I have a very broad banded sense of humour! It was as if the world had forgotten what love is, and the devastation that reigns when there is no love!

But then again, Lord, a cynic amongst us might say that most marriages (hopefully outside the confines of your church!) have a very strange notion of what true love is! I mean, if things keep going on the way they are, the marriage vows will soon be reduced to: "Do you, Thing Wasname, take Wanda Lust as your bride, to have and to hold as you had and held her loads of times before, for as long as you both shall live, or at least until someone else comes along?" What a sham!!

You only have to look at soap operas to find that love is severely misrepresented. They are so shallow and sad! (Apart from "Constipation Street", an every day story about people with bowel complaints. That's ok!) Now, we know, Lord, that love has many parts. Indeed, your word tells us in 1st Corinthians, chapter 13, "Love is patient, love is kind. It does not envy, it does not boast, it is not proud. It is not rude, it is not self-seeking, it is not easily angered, it keeps no record of wrongs. Love does not delight in evil but rejoices with the truth. It always protects, always trusts, always hopes, always perseveres. Love never fails!"

Love on T.V. would only demonstrate one or two of these parts in a relationship but never the whole picture, and hardly ever perseverance in the shape of faithfulness! (T.V. concentrates on all the negatives instead.) Oh, that the church will never be like that, Lord. We'd have to change our choruses if we did. We'd have "I tolerate you with the tolerance of the Lord!" and "Let there be no envy shared among us!" And of course "Amazing kindness, oh what unselfishness!" And what about the hymns? Love divine would become "Trust divine" or "Hope divine!" As much that these are good parts of love, they fall well short of the whole!

Love is like a precious jewel which is multi-faceted. All the sides combine to make the object of beauty, and the whole is not complete without them!

Also, you have commanded us to love our neighbour as we love ourselves. Does this mean that if we eat too much, drink too much or smoke, thereby generally abusing our bodies, we can nip next door and abuse our neighbours too? I should think not! But just in case, it's just as well my neighbour's thin, teetotal and doesn't smoke! I'm safe!

But you go on to instruct us to love our enemies. This is a toughie, Lord! But if we're going to change this world for you, we must learn to embrace all your facets of love and exercise them.

I pray, Lord, that your church (and that's me included!) may learn and adopt all your unselfish love, and bestow all the many parts on each other, so that we can take it out into the world and show them the complete picture, just as you showed us how to love completely!
                              Amen!

DEAR LORD...
DINOSAURS, ALIENS AND WOMEN PRIESTS

Dear Lord,

I've just come back from the cinema after seeing "Jurassic Park". What a great movie! Mind you, I had a bit of stick for going. Eric Bristow thought I was wasting my time and money to watch "a load of codswallop". (I told him there's no fish in it!) Still, we've come on a long way. I remember the time, not so very long ago, when it was widely thought that cinemas were not places to be frequented by Christians. "Do not sit in the seat of the unrighteous!" was vehemently quoted. A tad too literally translated, I think. I mean to say, it's one thing to avoid the cinema, but what about public conveniences? You're out shopping one day and nature starts to call! Do we reach into our shopping bags and pull out our handy portaloo? I suggest not! Especially not in the Marks and Spencer food hall!

Maybe that's why Christians used to wear long dresses, or baggy trousers, so that their nappies wouldn't show! It couldn't have been very comfortable on those wooden pews! Not to mention the smell! I'm glad those days have gone, Lord. Otherwise, I would have to creep into the cinema in disguise, you know, rain mac with collar up, dark glasses, trilby, sit at the back in a dark corner, leave just before the end of the film, and all to watch "Bambi" without fear of condemnation!

Anyway, back to "Jurassic Park". As I've said, a brilliant film! You'd swear those dinosaurs were real! (Well, you wouldn't Lord, but I would!) But it did make me think. Did dinosaurs really exist? It seems that they did, especially when you see those grand constructions in museums! And it normally follows that if you find a giant fossilised skeleton basically intact, then it's not too hard to figure out what it used to look like! But there's no mention of them in your word, Lord!! I mean, if they existed, why didn't Noah think to include a couple on the ark? Mind you, he was six hundred years old. He may have forgotten them! But what if he hadn't? I can picture it now. Noah turns to his wife and says, "Just keep those T-Rex's away from the Do-Do's! We don't want the same thing to happen as when we put them next to the Unicorns, do we? God will be livid when He finds out about that!" And when Noah saw the dove approach the ark carrying a sprig of olive branch in its beak, was he disheartened when a rogue pterodactyl swooped down from the sky and gobbled up the dove before it had a chance to tweet "DRY LAND!" I don't think so! Still, Hollywood would have a field day if it were true!

"Almighty productions present, NOAH, played by Charlton Heston, Noah's wife, played by Racquel Welch, Pterodactyl noises by Percy Edwards! Oh, how we could rewrite history!

But what about secret history? You know Lord, the things that have happened that "they", whoever "they" are, have "hushed-up?"

I'm talking Aliens Lord! From little green men from Mars intent on conquering the Earth, through E.T., to big, purple blobs that absorb humans! I mean, if they exist, then you would know because you created them! And is it so wacky to presume that within the billions of stars that light up our skies each night, (that is unless it's raining!) there aren't just a few planets spaced apart which hold some form of life? All this space and just little old us? But again, there's no mention of them in your word! Maybe if there was, we would read in the temptation of Jesus, "Then the devil took Him to the holy city and had Him stand on the highest point of the temple. 'If you are the Son of God,' he said, 'throw yourself down. For it is written: He will command His aliens concerning you, and they will give you a rocket pack so that you will not strike your foot against a stone.'" No, no!

And was Jonah really swallowed by a whale, or was he abducted by a U.F.O., and after carrying out strange experiments, they erased his memory and dumped him on the road to Ninevah? Not in your Bible, Lord! But many people believe they exist. Most believe that dinosaurs existed. But the world has such trouble believing that You exist! That just doesn't make sense. Some believe in the power of crystals, pyramids, Tarot cards, the stars, and yet they think that You and all your works are far-fetched? Incredible!

Some even believe that there is a Loch Ness monster! (Is there a Loch Ness monster? Again, you would know Lord, being the creator of all things!)

Why is it that this monster, or dinosaurs or aliens aren't mentioned in your word? Could it be because none of them really matter to the life you want for us? In your great commission, they are irrelevant! Jesus didn't stand at Bethany and declare, "Go out into all the world and make disciples of all nations, not forgetting Mars, but watch yourself around that Loch Ness 'cause there's a wee timorous beasty amongst the waters!"

He didn't because they have nothing to do with your plan! On the other hand, your word does mention witchcraft and the occult to warn us not to involve ourselves with it. They are negative satanic things which can affect the life you wish for us. But as for these other things, whether they exist or not is irrelevant! Does it then follow, Lord, that you haven't mentioned women priests in your word because the fact that they are women is irrelevant? They are human beings, like the rest of us, and are just as worthy of your blessing and carrying out your will as the next man, or woman for that matter! But what a fuss there is over them! I've heard of people leaving their church just because of this issue. But up till now, they've been perfectly content where they were and have been benefiting from their relationships and trust built up within. Suddenly, it's not good enough - and it hasn't even got a woman priest! It all seems such nonsense! If I understand it correctly Lord, before all this, the woman could do all the priestly duties except bless the communion. And yet when we sneeze, do we bat an eyelid if a woman says "Bless you!" No we do not! Besides, you have made us all equal. We are all able to do your will, and surely there shouldn't be much fuss if someone wants to proclaim blessings on us, be it male or female! And we know it is your delight to bless us, and your will for us to bless each other. So, I thank you Lord that just as dinosaurs, aliens and Loch Ness monsters are irrelevant, so is whether a priest is a woman or not of no consequence to your plan, just as long as she follows your will!

And may that be true for us all!

Amen!

DEAR LORD...
GREAT AND MIGHTY WARRIORS

Dear Lord,

I thank you that you are not bothered much by mistakes! I mean, we're all fallible (except you, Lord!) and any one of us is capable of the odd gaff or two. And Lord, I'm grateful that your grace covers us in these situations when we make utter fools of ourselves!

Yes Lord, I know I'm prone to forget things (except your love, mercy and grace) and this gets me into a bit of bother. I mean, remember the first month or so of my becoming a church usher. I had a bit of a Gideon experience. There I was, minding my own business, helping in the book shop whilst the church was waging spiritual warfare, praying against the proposed opening of a "porn shop" in the village, when I saw a great light shining down upon me. So, it was a torch light belonging to Sue, the floor ministry person, wondering what I was doing in that dark cupboard. I wasn't hiding Lord, honest. I was just fetching, er, things! Then, Sue proclaimed loudly, "Oh great and mighty usher!" I looked about! "Me?" I said. (There was only me in the cupboard.) "Yes!" she replied. "You will make a fine usher! Get thee hence to the platform!" I got me hence to the platform most hastily, and on arrival there to, I was verily bestowed with a job description! I read it. Mostly harmless, but then...."Get to church half an hour before it starts"...? But Lord, you know I like my sleep! Still, it looked acceptable, so I signed up. But let's be frank! My first day was hardly an auspicious occasion. First, I had to count how many people were seated upstairs during the service. Well, Lord, it was like doing one of those sums in junior school: Johnny has twenty five apples, he gives six to Freddy, and seven to Rebecca. Steven gives Johnny nineteen apples but eight are rotten and must be thrown away, etc, etc. How many apples does Johnny have left? Why can't people sit still? They were up and down, up and down! No sooner do I have a good count going when someone decides to go to the loo and a new person appears. Very confusing! And they don't like me looking at them. They must feel that I'm checking up on them. God's holy bouncer!

Make sure they're listening, eyes closed during prayers! And when I do eventually arrive at a total, I'm asked how many were children! A disaster! But then there's the communion. How was I to know that Jose' had run out of bread and was getting some more? Does it really matter if people drink the wine first? I don't know! And imagine dropping the collection basket!

Still, we'll have a continually rich church Lord, if only because of the money that irretrievably fell down the grating!

But the worst thing was the alter call duty! People went forward in response. I took my place behind this chap before I was left with only Mrs. Waters. A smart move, I thought. He stands with his hands in the air as we all sing this chorus. Pastor Parcel approaches him, lays his hands on him and starts to pray. The man wobbles. Here comes the plop! I'm ready! But no, he falls to his knees in tears. Then he gets into a crouching position. He wobbles a bit more! I'm ready! No plop! Then, up he stands! No tears now. It seems he is reconciled with you Lord. He raises his hands in worship. The altar call finishes. Pastor encourages us all to stay where we were and join in with the praise. And so I do! I like the chorus. I close my eyes and raise my hands. It was then that I felt something brush past me and I hear a dull thud on the floor! I open my eyes. The chap is on the floor beside me! I wasn't ready for him. Missed! Later, I apologised to him as I helped him off the floor and into the ambulance. Well, it was the least I could do. So, Lord, not a good start as an usher.

But you know that we make mistakes and you don't hold them against us, as long as we learn from them! Like the first time I thought I heard your voice! It was during a trip to St. Pauls' cathedral. We were inside, quite high up, looking down at the marble floor with only a slender length of railing between us and the fifty foot drop to oblivion. (I don't like heights Lord! Well, when I say I don't like heights, I mean I don't like falling from them!) So here I am, fighting my fear, high up inside the cathedral, when I hear a soft, gentle voice in my ear say, "Jump!" I looked around. There was no one else near me. Then the voice came again, "Jump!" I thought you were testing my faith Lord. (I would have failed miserably because there was no way I was going to jump.) Again the quiet voice, "Jump!" How was I to know I was in the whispering gallery! I thought it was you, when it was Tony all along, whispering against the wall by the entrance. What a wally! What a relief! But under the circumstances, an understandable mistake! Not like the one I made last week. As you know Lord, we had a baptismal service and I was asked to turn off the water heater in the pool half an hour prior to the dunking. Unfortunately, I forgot. Everybody thought that the people being baptised had a lovely spiritual glow when they came out of the water. Glow? They were being poached! The water was boiling! It was the quickest baptismal service I've ever seen! Twenty five people in seven minutes flat. A record! But a dreadful mistake!

I thank you Lord, that like Gideon, you see us as we are to become, not the mess we are now. We are like lumps of clay for you, the potter, to mould. And you see the vessels of your will that we will become when you have finished your work in us. You are more concerned with our heart than our hands; our attitude more than our actions! Thank you that your grace covers our mistakes and replaces them with love.

All praise and glory to your name!

DEAR LORD...
A FATHER'S LOVE

Dear Lord,

I'm sorry that I haven't spoken to you for a while. I've been far too busy doing my own thing, caught up in my own affairs, and I've neglected the most important area in my life, that is, maintaining my relationship with you! I have no excuse! Someone once told me, "If you're too busy to pray, you're **TOO** busy!" So, I apologise, Lord.

It seems that there are times in my walk where I am still very much a child. I remember when I was small, my father took me out for a walk. Well, he walked! I was pushed on my scooter. "Faster!" I'd shout with glee, and he would oblige, much to my joy. Suddenly, I saw something glistening up ahead, and thinking it may be something precious, I scooted ahead of my father, further and further away until I reached the object of my attention. It was just a piece of broken glass reflecting in the sunlight. When I turned to tell my father, he wasn't beside me. I felt afraid. But then I looked back and saw him waiting where I had left him, ready to move down a different path. But instead of rushing back, I pretended to cry and shouted for him to come and get me. Quite rightly, he told me that I'd gone under my own steam and I could return the same way! "But I'm tired!" I cried.

With much protestation and sulking, I started back and eventually reached him, but the grumpiness soon disappeared when he gave me a hug and I felt safe again. And Lord, there are so many times that we have been like that! You have been encouraging me on forward into areas of your way, much to my joy. Then, I will rush off in my own power and find disappointment. I would feel sad and miss you, for you were not with me. But I know that I can find you if I go back to where we were. I don't like going back, but I must. And when I reach you again, I'm so glad as you wrap your loving arms around me. And away we go together, Father and son. Thank you also that you do not move down the different path without me, but wait for me to catch up.

I suppose that the discipline of consistent prayer is a sign of maturity. The apostle Paul says in his letter to the Corinthians, "When I was a child, I talked like a child, I thought like a child, I reasoned like a child. When I became a man, I put childish ways behind me." There are times when I am very much a child and it's time I grew up.

But I thank you that you have a father's love for me. Being a parent, I can appreciate the love and care a father has for his child. But I also know of the frustration a child can cause!

When my son was born, my wife and I took turns to bottle feed him through the night. I had the One o'clock shift, and she fed him at five! This arrangement suited me as I normally watch television until about that time! One night, Timothy awoke and I prepared his milk. We sat together as I fed him, but for some reason, he wasn't taking it properly. I persevered, knowing the importance of regular feeds. For an hour, I struggled to get him to drink his milk. At two thirty, and with only half the contents of the bottle gone, I'd had enough! I was too tired to fight! I picked him up to wind him. A few burps later, I felt a warm, wet sensation running down my back! I was soaked in regurgitated milk! I took it personally. Something inside me snapped! I held him up at arms length, out of harm's way, and I pounded my feet on the floor in frustration, while I emitted a tortured sound resembling a pig giving birth! My wife heard the noise and was naturally concerned, thinking some wild animal was loose downstairs. And she would be right! Me!

She appeared on the landing to find me in tears, and Timothy gurgling happily away in the knowledge of a job well done! I felt totally exhausted and helpless. What a waste of time! I looked across at my adversary. I was too tired to seethe. (I was also starting to smell!) Timothy looked back at me and smiled! My heart melted! All the anguish faded away under the winsome little gaze of my son. How could I be angry with this beautiful person. "Are you alright?" my wife asked, coming down the stairs. I looked again at Timothy and stroked his soft hair. "Yes!" I sighed. "We're fine!"

And there's often times, Lord, when both kids have run me ragged to the point of various punishments. (Sent to bedroom, smacks, no children's t.v. for a week, forced to eat peas, listen to me sing, etc.) But when I look in on them before I turn in for the night and I see them sleeping so sweetly in their beds, my heart fills anew with love for them, and I feel a right rotter for some of the things I've said or done. (Although I always remind myself of why!)

And surely this is just a small part of the overwhelming depth of love that you, our father have for us. Whatever love I have for my children, you can multiply a hundred times for your children.

Thank you for your father's love, Lord, and the opportunity to demonstrate it to my kids, that they may also experience the love from the Father's heart!

Amen.

DEAR LORD...
LOONIES!!

Dear Lord,

Doesn't it ever bother you that Christians are portrayed by television as loonies? If the plot of a play calls for someone to be a Christian, they are either a hypocrite, a bigot, a fanatic, or all three! When I watch T.V., I can always tell the Christian. She's the one that says one thing and does another. He's the one who is totally intolerant to other people's views, but is quite unreasonable in his own! They are the ones, dare I say it, "hell-bent" on world domination in the name of God! And if they're "born-again" Christians, they are barking up a gum tree! Why, oh why aren't Christians portrayed the way they really are? Lord, I know there are people in your church who are a bit like that but they aren't the norm! We've all seen T.V. shows where someone will stand up and make a bit of a fool of themselves, and then proclaim that they did it for Christ, causing us to groan inwardly! But most of your people aren't like that. People don't seem to realise that Christians are just ordinary folk with extra-ordinary help! We all go through the same trials and tribulations, but because we stand for a higher cause than the world can ever match, we are judged more severely. If a Christian is hammering a nail and hits his thumb, letting out a curse before he knew what he was saying, or if he totally neglected to help someone in need, he or she would very soon receive a fierce reproach, "And I thought you were a Christian!!" But can we turn this around? The next time I see a non-Christian do something good, I'll yell, "And I thought you were a heathen!"

So with this in mind, I face a quandary! Thanks to television (and the odd quack within the church) your people have received a bad press. And as people equate your church with you, Lord, what we do colours what people think of you! I've often heard stories of people who joined a church because of a need you were fulfilling, only for them to leave because the pastor had dealt harshly with them. When I speak to them now, they say that You dealt harshly with them! They have got your church's actions mixed up with your actions. Most of the time, they're the same, but they can differ, as I'm sure you know, otherwise you wouldn't have to correct us and we wouldn't need you so much! But as we are your ambassadors, this is quite an enormous responsibility. And we become ambassadors for Christ the moment we give our lives to you! The trouble there is that we are very much like children at that point and we have to mature. This takes time and we will frequently blow it along the way, just as a child makes mistakes and learns. Thank you, Lord, that you don't hold this against us, but encourage us forward, learning our lessons. But in the world's eyes, once a thief, always a thief! Once a liar, always a liar! Regardless of all the good things you may have done! No forgiveness! No absolution! Ironically, the world that treats us so harshly is equally as guilty of hypocrisy, bigotry and fanaticism as we are. The difference is that with your help we are trying to do something about it! So, with the world having such a "loony" view of your church (your living church at least), should we normalise your services to make us more acceptable? Would people be more willing to come to church if your body did less things to put them off? I mean Lord, when folk enter the doors of your dwelling place, do they see "normal" people?

What do they make of people speaking in tongues and other such gifts of the Spirit? They've got nothing "normal" to equate to where they are, so it must come across as being really weird! People plopping must be off-putting if you don't know why it happens! And tithing in the world's eyes just is not economical sense!

Why give it away just to get it back? Why not just hang on to it in the first place? Would we attract more people into your church if we "toned down" the service a bit, you know, not encourage plopping, whisper in tongues, forget tithing? Maybe we could re-write your Word to make it more "politically correct!" We could basically leave out most of Romans, especially where it speaks against the occult, homosexuality and sexual perversions. Remove the bits involving adultery, divorce and fornication, Lovely jubbly! (I wonder what sort of church we'd end up with then?)

Trouble is, world, the Lord God has written in Revelation that we are not to alter any of His words, haven't you, Lord! And if we altered your service that much, I'm not convinced that your Spirit would bother to turn up!

The conclusion to my quandary is that your normality is totally different to the normality of the world. It is what you ordain that is of utmost importance to us, more than anything else, because only your will naturally works. The world forces its ways and will on people, but your will and ways are natural to your creation. Unfortunately, the world either cannot or will not comprehend it! So how do we attract people into your church?

Well Lord, I haven't taken your Spirit into account very much so far, have I? And it's when I think back to why I first started going to church that I realise His importance. My conversion testimony is relatively boring, especially when compared to those of people you have saved on their death beds, etc, but I know that it's no less a miracle and cost just as much! I was just your average guy. I didn't lead what many would consider a life of sin (although life without you Lord is a life of sin!) I didn't take drugs, didn't smoke, nor drink too much (except on odd occasions), wasn't short of cash, had a good social life, didn't really need for much, or so I thought! I knew a bit about you Lord, but it was mostly inaccurate. I actually believed as a child that you were an old man in a wheel-chair, and waited at Sunday school for them to wheel you out. Well, they kept talking about you but I never saw you. And the Spirit was always referred to as "The Holy Ghost!" I'd seen a few horror movies and the "Ghost" bit stuck in my mind. I imagined the Spirit as a hooded monk, face hidden in shadow, mysteriously floating on mist. And when the Sunday school teachers said that the "Holy Ghost" came upon them, I was terrified! In my mind, He was quite a scary character that I certainly didn't want to meet! Not at all the "comforter and guide" I know now! And when the baby Jesus was born, I thought he was visited by the three wise men, who were Dracula, Frankenstein and Myrrh! I'd heard of the other two, but who was Myrrh? Strange visitors to the Holy of Holies! I thought that John the baptist was beheaded by "the Axe of the Apostles!"

I thought a lady vicar was a vixen! I thought that part of the Lord's prayer was "And lead us not into Thames Station!" And I believed that Christians were only to have one wife because monotony is good! (I didn't know what monogomy was!)

But as I grew up, these ideas didn't really alter much. What could I possibly benefit from knowing you? I really didn't know how much I needed you until I met you. It was during a time of great stress. My father was deadly ill, I was in the middle of my A-level exams, and I was at the end of my teenage years. I learnt to cope with all these problems by shutting off and not letting them affect me. I closed off my feelings! I didn't realise it but I was hardening my heart. But I started courting a lovely girl called Philippa who invited me to the church she attended. I went along, just to keep the peace (and the girl!) and entered the loony den! The guest speaker was American. This put me off from the start as I'd heard about American evangelists. But I stayed, watched, listened impassively, assessing, analysing, concluding but not feeling! I don't recall what he shared that night but I remember the affect after when he prayed with people. Suddenly, something in the room changed. People started crying! Men and women, who seemed quite ordinary just a few moments ago, started crying, but not with sorrow, but in joy! I could see it on their faces, tears streaming down their cheeks. Just real Joy! And my heart began to ache! It had been so long since I'd last felt joy. I didn't know at the time what was affecting those people but I wanted it! I had felt the move of your Spirit for the first time and I found it irresistible! And when I look back now, I remember that there was so much of that service I found unpalatable, but I couldn't resist your Spirit! And I wonder if they had "toned down" the service to normalise it, whether I would have received anything at all. You had prepared my heart for that moment, and it would have been a disaster if you weren't allowed to move as you wanted that night. You orchestrated the whole thing! All your people had to do was be obedient, worship you and take opportunities to share the good news when you present them, and you would do the rest. And now I don't worry how people view Christians. Nor am I too concerned with attracting people into your church. You make the preparation in people's hearts. It's up to us to prepare your dwelling place to receive your Spirit, and to share your word when they are listening. I thank you that we don't have to impress the world. We are not the alternative. Rather, the world is the alternative to your life. Giving our lives to you is the most natural thing we can do! It's a law of your nature! Just as a deep sea diver expects to float up the surface when he kicks off the weights around his feet, so is it natural to come into your presence when we kick off the chains of sin and give our hearts to you! We are designed to float. We are created to be in worshipful relationship with you Lord!

I thank you that you are a supernatural God, who works in the natural. I thank you that you allowed your Spirit to move me where nothing else could. And I thank you for your church, not perfect but endeavouring to be in faith; the natural environment for us to meet and worship you. Never let it change for the world's sake, Lord. Let us be happy to be fools for you.

Amen.

DEAR LORD...
ZITS

Dear Lord,

I don't mean to moan, especially not to you because I know that there's not much you can do about this, but why does this always happen to me? My problem? Well, you see, it's spots! Not like leopard spots, you understand, but zits! I don't mind having zits, Lord; I know everybody has them, but why is it that I appear to be the only one who has them right on the end of the nose? I can't have them conveniently hidden in the hair line, nor on the chest or legs, no! It's got to be right on the tip of my nose! I look like Rudolf's brother! It's a wonder I'm not permanently cross-eyed the way it draws my sight down onto it. It's like a flashing beacon! It's not even discreet! Spots are so insensitive. They take no account of your plans. They don't care if you're just about to have a passport photo taken! They just appear! Hello! Here I am! Just like a spoiled kid! Look at me! Look at me! And there it is, bright red and shiny with a lovely white top! And it attracts your gaze like a magnet. There's just no ignoring spots like these! I may as well wear a clown's nose! And I've noticed that the bigger the spot, the less likely it is that people will give you a big, welcoming hug at the door of church. They start to, then they see it! Here I am! Look out! (Now I know how the lepers felt!)

It reminds me of the time we had a visiting speaker with a massive boil on his cheek. It was a beauty! In the Miss Spot contest 1994, it was in the first three! He called people forward for prayer and as he lay hands on them, the boil burst, issuing forth a substance which had the front row reeling back in horror, tripping over those behind, sending two rows of people crashing to the floor! "What a mighty ministry he has!" We thought, as we saw what looked like thirty people simultaneously slain in the spirit! Unfortunately, this wasn't the case!

But spots have that effect on people! And this one's affecting me right now! I wouldn't be surprised if it started making "beep beep" noises! And when it does eventually erupt, it'll probably be as devastating as the time Mount St.Helens exploded in the U.S.A. a while ago! It'll take away half of my nose, and throw so much debris into the atmosphere that some parts of Russia won't see the sun for six months!

How do I get these blemishes Lord? I mean, did the Lord Jesus ever have spots? He grew up, went through puberty, suffered all the ravages that life could throw at Him, but was never known for His complexion! Jesus did not "blitz those Zits" with Biactol, nor did He cleanse His skin with Clearasil lotion! I have these products at hand to help me and yet I still become Job's stable-mate! And the Lord said to Abraham, "I will surely bless you and make your descendants as numerous as the stars in the sky and as the sand on the seashore, and as the spots on Terry's face!"

If you can't make out my features, just join the dots! Maybe it's just a physical representation of my impurity! (Maybe it's because I don't wash properly!) All I know is that it makes me very self-conscious.

But it's surprising how internal blemishes do that too Lord! You know, when you do something you shouldn't, or say something you regret. The next Sunday in church, you're convinced everyone knows what you've done! I feel so convicted. Of course, nobody does know, except you, but the truth has an uncanny knack of slipping out, even if the inquisitors are completely innocent. It's as if the whole conversation were directed by you, Lord, the one who knows all hearts!

Sin makes you self-conscious! An example of this was when Jennifer and I were invited to a meal at Pastor Parcel and his wife's! This was quite a daunting prospect! The Pastor and his wife? That holy man and woman of God request the "pleasure" of the company of me and my missus? (We're not worthy!) What would we talk about? I couldn't tell them any jokes for fear of "stepping over the mark!" (Why is it that when I try to remember a joke, I can only think of rude ones? I really must discourage Martin the music leader from telling me them!) And we didn't feel informed enough on church events to discuss them! And it didn't help that just before we arrived at their house, we had a blazing row over who'd left the freezer door open and let all the food defrost! Meeting Mr. and Mrs.Parcel after that was not something we relished, especially as the sermon last Sunday was an appeal for compassion to the starving in Africa and we'd just thrown out fifty pounds worth of food! Boy, did we feel convicted! It was as if we were covered in internal spots. The pastor and his wife would see through us immediately and have it fixed permanently in their minds what wasters we were! But we couldn't have been more wrong! It transpired that Tom and Pippa (as we now call them) had just had a similar blazing row about Tom's inability to fix a dripping tap, which due to his efforts became an ornamental fountain in the bathroom! I endeavoured to help, Lord, but not being much of a handy man either, we abandoned the sink, shut off the water supply, and sipped on wine and Perrier for the rest of what turned out to be a fantastic evening. We discovered that this mighty man and woman of God were also just a man and a woman like Jen and me! We eventually stopped nattering at one in the morning and said our farewells in the knowledge that we had all got to know each other better.

But when I think, Lord, I realise that self-consciousness is a waste of time! Whether it's due to acne or to sin, worrying about what other people think of me is ridiculous. It is what you think of me, Lord, that is all important! And I thank you that you love me however I look and whatever I say or do! You know my heart and see my imperfections. You know I'm not perfect, so why should I worry if your people discover that too? (Just as I'm discovering that about them!)

I thank you that you showed me the pastor and his wife are just people, as is your congregation. And I thank you for allowing me and my wife to be people loved by you!

Amen!

DEAR LORD...
THE POEM

Dear Lord,

I know it must be strenuous on times, keeping creation in order, being mindful of us all, etc. So I thought I'd write you a poem about my day. Hopefully, you'll enjoy it! I know you like us to be creative, just as I enjoy my children's creativity, except when it means felt-pen marks all over my walls! Anyway, here it is.

"I woke up nice and sprightly for the cricket match,
but I had to sort out my freezer 'cause it's got a faulty catch!
I phoned up the insurers and told them of my claim.
My estimate was honest 'cause lying's not my game!

But you'd be surprised how many people thought that I was mad.
They said I should say it cost double.
There's profit to be had!
If I'm honest, I was tempted! I mean, who would know?

But you would, wouldn't you Father?
I couldn't sink that low!
I thought I'd be rewarded for my honest deed,
but I found that I was wrong as I watched the day proceed.

It started bad at breakfast when I sat at my bacon and eggs,
except the cat had eaten them and left me with the dregs!
Still hungry, I left for the pavilion.
I'd try out my new cricket shoe!

But sheppie my dog had surprised me,
and I stepped in a load of dog's pooh!
When I finally found my white trainers,
I left for my cricketing date,

but traffic and a flat tyre ensured I was really quite late!
They put me to bat quite early,
and I thought I'd show them some pluck,
but the umpire ruled L.B.W. The opposition had me out for a duck!

Not surprisingly, all went against us.
In the end, it was a bit of a rout.
They declared at six hundred and seven,
but the game was beyond any doubt!

Well, life could be worse, I reckoned.
As we left, we started to sing,
but I nearly choked at my motor
when I saw the huge dent in the wing!

'That was it!' I declared in my temper,
and a strangled yell rose from my throat.
I would have said something I shouldn't,
but I saw on my wind-screen a note.

It was a letter from the car-bashing culprit,
saying how sorry he was for my ails,
and he left his name and car number,
and all his insurance details.

Thank goodness he left me his ticket.
Now everything could be put right!
But it all could have been so much different,
I thought as I drove home that night.

It seems that me and that un-careful driver
have morals of one accord,
Honesty is always the best policy,
and truth is its own reward!

Now to even up my day,
there's just two things I must do.
I must eat my cat for breakfast,
and flush sheppie down the loo!

Amen.

DEAR LORD...
THY KINGDOM COME

Dear Lord,

If a tree falls in a forest and there's nobody around to hear it, does it make a sound? It can't really happen because trees don't just fall! Somebody must have chopped it down! Anyway, I ask because I've just seen this film "On the Beach" where nuclear fall-out killed everyone on earth and the world became a desolate place. A bit morbid, I know, but it made me ask "If there's nobody around to witness it, would TIME exist?" Did you create time so that we could be mortal? And is eternity only possible when there is no time? You see, I'm wondering what it will be like in your kingdom, Lord! The book of Revelation gives us a clue.

There'll be lots of praise and worship. A bit like the spring harvest praise weekend we just had at the local Butlins camp! I must be honest, when I heard it was to be held at Butlins, all sorts of ideas sprang to mind. We could have the "Reverend knobbly knees competition." Pastor Parcel would have a good chance in that! Then, there's the "Most glamorous Elder contest." No takers in our church, I'm afraid! "The Joseph and Mary donkey derby!" That's a good one! In the morning, we'd wake up to strains of worship songs over the tannoys, accompanied by hearty "Morning praisers!" We could have family baptisms in the swimming pool. Alter calls on the trampolines, so that when people "plop", they'd come straight back up for more! There'd be "Chorus Kareoke evenings!" Vicars and tarts fancy dress! (Maybe we'll give this one a miss!) How about a "Conscience wresting championship!" (I'd be good at that!) Oh, and "Hymn number Bingo!" All the sixes, 666, the antichrist, Christmas day number 25, Holy Trinity number 3... "CHURCH!" Somebody shouted "CHURCH!"

Whatever it would be, it would be fun! And it was! Thousands of Christians together under one roof. We had a brilliant time! There was a real party atmosphere with your Spirit the guest of honour! And I wondered if your kingdom would be similar, though miles better!

When your kingdom comes, Lord, it'll be party time for the chosen! And because we're all in glory, time would no longer exist! Partying for eternity! It'll be terrific! I've been to a few do's that have been so good that I've wished they didn't have to end, and this one won't!! Hallelujah!

Let your kingdom come, Lord, and your will be done,
for ever and ever,
Amen!

DEAR LORD...
PERSEVERANCE AND HOPE

Dear Lord,

The apostle Paul says in his letter to the Romans, "Suffering brings perseverance, perseverance brings character, and character, hope!" I thank you for those encouraging words because suffering I have been! Some times, Lord, I seem to be dogged by mishap. I've already told you about my trouble with spots, and so I thought a bit of a sun tan would give me a bit of colour and improve my complexion. Well, I don't know how I did it but I've managed to tan just the left side of my face.

The right side is untouched. It's as if the ozone layer decided to slip aside for a second like a huge camera shutter and the giant flash bulb in the sky went off just as I was looking right. Zap! Out comes the picture. Multi-coloured face! I've got to try and have a permanent blush to even it up! I can do that by remembering something that happened to me whilst in school. As a student, the only thing I was ever any good at was athletics. Long distance, to be exact! I was in top form and the favourite to win the 1500 metres at the school fete. It was quite a jolly affair with stalls set up around the field and jazz bands performing in the centre of the running track. The apostle Paul has said that we are to run the straight race until we win the prize, and as this race started, I certainly had my mind on the prize. I had established a bit of a lead but I knew the others weren't far behind. As I glanced back to see where the second placed boy was, I didn't notice members of the jazz band wandering idly over the track. Crash! Boom! I'd never seen the inside of a bass drum before. Very interesting! And those kazoos can really cut into your legs, you know! Unfortunately, no prize for me! I suppose the lesson is to always know where you're going. Thanks Paul! But again, mishaps occurred from an early age. And when I try to do good things, it sometimes goes wrong. Like the time Tudor Toffee's son was sitting upstairs during a service and leant too far over the balcony rail. Pastor Parcel noticed him and nearly choked as the boy started to fall. Fortunately, the boy managed to hold onto the rail with one hand. This bought us time. Instantly, I sprang into action. Indiana Jones would have been proud of me. I flew down the steps to the rail, brandishing my bullwhip. Well, it was a speaker cable really but it made a handy replacement. My intention was to flip the cable around the boy's wrist and pull him to safety, as our hero did in "The Temple of Doom!" Unfortunately, I lack the skills of Dr.Jones and succeeded in cracking the whip painfully on the lad's hand, causing him to let go! Disaster! Thank you, Lord, that Jose' is the church football team's goalkeeper and had the presence of mind to be under him and made the perfect catch. But it didn't end there! Jose' then bounced the boy twice on the floor and booted him up to the back of the church! (Not really, Lord, but the thought is funny!)

Paul again teaches to "never tire of doing good things!" And so perseverance is called for, particularly when I mess up.

Someone once said to me that the sign of a good life is when you can look back and say, "I did what I believed was right at the time!" Well, that's me! But whether you consider that the sign of a righteous life, I don't know! There were times when I felt I was one of the unluckiest guys around. But really, I know how fortunate I am to be one of your sons - an heir to your throne! I thank you for the privilege of being adopted by you. I really do appreciate it, Lord. You have put my life in order, even though I still make mistakes. And thank you that you've built perseverance into my life, because as Paul says, my sufferings bring on perseverance, and that gives me character. And that character gives me hope! And it's that hope that we all live for!

It's comforting to know, Lord, that every time I mess up, I can have hope in you! That is so wonderful to know! So until the next time I goof, Thank you, Lord, for listening!

DEAR LORD...
GATES OF PRAISE

Dear Lord,

I've just come back from the T.V. studios in Bristol where they're shooting the latest episode of "CHURCHUALTY." It's a Christian version of "Casualty" except that the staff treat spiritual accidents instead of physical. This time, they treated two people for apathy, one for depression and another for demonic possession. The ambulances have a siren which goes, "GLORY, GLORY!" I'm not sure if the programme will catch on but we'll see! Anyway, on our way home, we crossed the Severn Bridge. But first, we had to pay the toll. If we didn't pay, we didn't cross. And this got me thinking, Lord. Pastor Parcel always says that "He who controls the gates to the city, controls the city!" And here it was in action. We had to fulfil certain obligations before we could proceed. Your word declares, Lord, that the gates to your city are praise. We reach the gates with thanksgiving, but only enter the courts through the gates with praise. This makes sense to me. I heard the tale of a chap who was eating his tea, when someone knocked on his door. When he answered it, a giant cockroach barged in, beat him up, ate his food, trashed the house, then left. The poor chap was taken to the Accident and Emergency department of the local hospital and told the doctor what had happened. The doctor wasn't surprised. He'd heard there was a NASTY BUG going about!! A silly joke, but it illustrated a point!

If someone knocked on my door and was abusive to me when I answered, I would soon replace the door in their face! But if, when the door was opened, they spent a time saying how nice my garden was, how well I'd painted the window frames, and how pebble-dashing the brickwork had improved the house no end, I'd surely invite them indoors to praise me some more about my home-made fitted kitchen and formica worktops. A little bit of praise goes a long way. (A fact which my wife could well take note of next time a cupboard door falls off or the worktop starts peeling!) And if anyone is worthy of our praise, it's you, Lord!

I will enter your gates with thanksgiving in my heart. I will enter your courts with praise. I will say this is the day that the Lord has made. I will rejoice for you have made me glad! Thank you, Lord.

Amen.

DEAR LORD...
FASTING

Dear Lord,

I just want to thank you, Lord that although some things you ask us to do appear very strange, you have a purpose for everything and a reasoning that's accurate. I refer, of course, to the events of the last few days. We need a new building for our expanding church, as you know, Lord, and we have found the right place in agreement with you. Now that we've found it, we must pay for it. So, Pastor Parcel called for a three-day fast to breakthrough any financial constraints, both corporately and personally. I had never fasted before but I really felt that I wanted to take part this time. But I didn't know what it was all about, how it worked, and to what extent I should abstain from food. So I consulted Martin, the worship leader, about the latter point. Always a bit of a wag, he told me that I was only allowed fresh goat's milk three times a day. I thought I had problems straight away. Where would I find a goat? Thankfully, he was jesting and informed me that most people allowed themselves tea, coffee or fruit juices, while others just drank water. This was a disappointment as I'd just stocked up with Complan, Slim fast milk shakes and Minestrone soup! So I compromised and stayed with tea and orange juice. So, as day one approached, I stuffed myself silly, hoping that it would give me a good shove into my fast voyage. But "fast" it was not! I didn't really miss breakfast, lunch was tolerable, but tea time was murder! The trouble is, Lord, that I just love eating! It's a pastime of mine; a hobby, if you like, and when I go home from work, it's something I really look forward to! But not today, nor for the next two days! Then I realised that I should be using the time I would normally spend eating in prayer. So I did! And very good it was too! As you know, Lord, I don't really spend much time in prayer, so this was quite a diversion from the usual. I also decided to study fasting, to discover what it was about. My Bible took me through various fasts, and I found an interesting few verses in Matthew chapter six, verse sixteen onwards. It said,

"When you fast, do not look sombre as the hypocrites do, for they disfigure their faces to show men they are fasting. I tell you the truth, they have received their reward in full. But when you fast, put oil on your head and wash your face so it will not be obvious to men that you are fasting, but only to your father, who is unseen; and your father, who sees what is done in secret, will reward you!"

So, I washed my face and started to rifle about in the garage for a tin of three-in-one oil. Thankfully, Jennifer stopped me as I was about to daub my bonce in crude, and convinced me that it wasn't necessary.

Day two arrived and I felt much better at breakfast time. At lunch time, I found a quiet corner by a window and prayed. I felt an overwhelming peace flow over me. Then I felt my gaze being attracted out of the window. There, drifting lazily in the sky, was a seagull. It effortlessly soared, round and round, not beating its wings, riding on the thermals. And then I heard you tell me that this is where you want me to be. The thermals represent your will, and if I stay in your will, then you will hold me up and support me totally, carrying me forward and onwards, with little effort from me. This was a wonderful revelation, and certain confirmation of the solution to my own personal quandary. Thank you, Lord, that you spoke so clearly to me then.

But you weren't the only one speaking to me! Satan was having a go too! First, he tried telling me that there was no way I could do without food for three days. Then he said that the empty feeling in the pit of my stomach was a tumour. He went on to say that I need food to neutralise the acid in my stomach, or I'll develop ulcers! I was already a bit irritable and he tried all ways to make me lose my temper. Whenever something taxing happened, a voice in my head said, "You shouldn't have to cope with all this AND fast at the same time!" By day two, he was sympathising with me, congratulating me and saying, "Well done! Two days is fabulous. You don't have to prove anything else now. EAT!" Of course Lord, I denied him again and again, because I know that if Satan tries to stop you from doing something, it's because it will be of great benefit, and to his cost! So I told him to shut it and went off to housegroup. Thankfully, everyone there was experiencing the same things, but we were all resolute and rejoicing. The hunger pangs had gone. It's at times like these that I can really appreciate people like Eric and Mrs.Waters, who for all their stuffiness, are obedient to you, Lord.

As we prayed quietly in your Spirit, I was suddenly reminded of Romans chapter eight, verse twenty six, "In the same way, the Spirit helps us in our weakness. We do not know what we ought to pray for, but the Spirit himself intercedes for us with groans that words cannot express!"

Well Lord, whether we were praying in your Spirit or not, there was certainly a lot of groaning going on. The cumulative sounds of ten people's stomachs gurgling was amazing! It was really loud, and funny! We were like an orchestra, with the ladies being the strings and the men the percussion. At one stage, the sound was slightly reminiscent of "Bind us together!" But not quite! My stomach, surprisingly, was the exception. Forty eight hours into the fast and it hadn't made a sound! I can only deduce that it was so stunned and shocked that it couldn't find its voice! By lunch time on day three, however, it had come to its senses and was blustering away at me all afternoon. Whether it was because I knew I was breaking my fast that evening at church, which wasn't too long away, or because someone beside me was eating minced beef pie and chips, I don't know! (It's strange, but biscuits, cakes or crisps held no appeal. But I was really tempted by pasties and pies!) But I ignored my gastric friend and stayed strong all the way.

When evening came, I set off for church full of joy and happiness. I'd done it! There's one in the eye for Satan! And we had broken through, personally and corporately. Praise you, Lord, for your goodness, mercy and grace!

But what a noise a church full of gurgling stomachs makes. I suppose that just as you have your word, The Holy Bible, and then your Amplified Bible, we had gurgling in housegroup, and amplified gurgling in church.

And Pastor Parcel's sermon didn't help. We were due to break fast when he shared, "And so, my friends, DOUGHNUT tempt the Lord into help, but rather CURRY His FLAVOUR in times of trouble when the CHIPS are down, such as when you've made a HASH of things and are in a bit of a STEW! When you are SANDWICHED between the devil and the deep blue sea, and believe you are about to receive your just DESSERTS, PLAICE yourself in the Lord's hands. He will BEEF up your courage, just when you think you CARROT take any more. He will

BRAISE you up before the ROAST of ROASTS. He will encourage you and EGG you on. And when He BACONS you, respond, and you will find that there is so MUSHROOM in your heart for His love!"

Thanks, Pastor! That really got us going! And even the choruses started to take on new meaning. We sang all the normal ones, but somehow, the words began to change. Instead of "I see Jesus in your eyes!" we had "I see cheeses in you pies!" It didn't end there! We had "Peas (peace) like a river, Loaves (love) like a mountain!"

"I'll eat mince pies (I will arise) and go forth in the name of the Lord of toasts (hosts)!"

"Purify my tart(heart)!"

"My knife (life) is in food (you) Lord!"

"Father in oven (heaven) how we love you!"

"Father, you are my chicken portion in this life!"

"I eat liver (I live) because he is risen!"

"All hail the lamb!" (No comment!)

We were really starving by the time the soup arrived. But Lord, it has really taught me a lot. I've learnt that fasting humbles me and I reached the point of total surrender to you far quicker than ever before. I've only been there before due to having blown it and run out of ideas on how to solve a problem. That was when I totally listened or been in a position to acknowledge how much I needed your help. But fasting took me straight there, without the problems! I've never seen that before.

The apostle Paul says in Romans twelve, "Therefore, I urge you, brother, in view of God's mercy, to offer your bodies as living sacrifices, holy and pleasing to God, this is you spiritual act of worship. Do not conform any longer to the pattern of this world, but be transformed by the renewing of your mind. Then you will be able to test and approve what

God's will is - His good, pleasing and perfect will." And this tied in with the gull you showed me and what you said later. My fasting was my spiritual act of worship, which was transforming my mind, allowing me to discover what your will is for me.

And I thank you Lord that after seventy two hours of abstinence, I can say that I honestly know your good, pleasing and perfect will for my life, and I will rest in you. Take me Father. Carry me along.
Thank you Lord.

Amen.

DEAR LORD...
GETTING BACK INTO SHAPE

Dear Lord,
    I've blown it again! Please forgive me! I was at housegroup on Tuesday night. All the regulars were there, and we got into a discussion on smoking! Now, as you know, Lord, I've never smoked and don't particularly like the habit, but I understand how addictive it can be, and how hard it is to give up. But just then, Mrs.Waters started on about how he couldn't understand why people defiled their bodies with nicotine. Well Lord, change "nicotine" for "haute cuisine" and there's a whole lot of defilement going on in Mrs.Waters' household, but she just can't see it and it's this hypocrisy that makes me see red. Your Word says, "before you comment on the twig in your neighbour's eye, take the plank out of your own!" (or something like that!) and so I felt I could stay silent no longer.

    She began by saying that she could never smoke because her body is a temple. I commented that it was more like a cathedral, where she worshipped the great god Grub! Lord of lunch, Deity of dinner and Sovereign of supper!

    She hastily made up the excuse that she had a glandular problem. "Salivary gland?" I ventured. By now, it was too late to go back. She stated that all she needed was a little bit of exercise. I put it to her that it required a lot more than that. After all, you don't hear of too many Jane Fonda work-out tapes being sold in places like Ethiopia. No mention of any Jennie Craig clinics opening there either, and yet the people are all painfully thin. I suggested a decrease in food input.

    "Look," she said, "I am just an ordinary person like everyone else. I have two eyes, two ears....."

    "Two chins!" I countered. This brought a gasp from the others.
Mrs Waters glared, and pointing accusingly at me, she yelled, "Two faces!"

As I began to protest, Neil and Pat thankfully stepped in and reminded us of grace and tolerance. This left us both a bit ashamed, and hence this prayer, Lord.

But the argument made me think about my general fitness, and how my spirit man mirrors my flesh man. To keep my flesh man in the pink, I need to eat healthy food and exercise regularly. So too with my spirit man. We all like junk food, but if we lived on it, we'd become very ill. And to be honest, Lord, I've not been feeding my spirit man with Your Word, nor other healthy food lately. More a lot of junk! Exercising my faith hasn't been a priority either. I've been like the fat chap sitting on the park bench, eating another pie, watching the joggers go by.

I've become a biblical blobby, a pentecostal porker, a holy rolypoly!

It's time I got back into shape, both flesh and spirit, starting today - right after tea!

Amen.

DEAR LORD...
A LIGHT IN DARKNESS

Dear Lord,

We've just had our annual church bonfire night party. Most of the fellowship were there either trying to get the bonfire going, buttering rolls for the hot dogs, or stirring the soup. Of course, there were objectors to our night of frivolity. Eric Bristow thought we were, and I quote, "frittering away valuable church funds to celebrate a disgraced terrorist, when it could be better spent elsewhere!"

It brought to mind that time when You, Lord Jesus, were at a dinner thrown in Your honour by Mary, Martha and Lazarus. It's in the Gospel of John, and I've brought it up to date.

"Then Mary took out a catherine wheel, and upon nailing it securely to a post, she didst beckon the Lord to light it. And the house was filled with light and smoke, and the crowd didst say 'oooh!' and 'ahhh!' But one of His disciples, Judas, objected. 'Why wasn't this catherine wheel sold and the money given to the poor?'"

Not that I'm saying that Eric is anything like Judas Iscariot. But as it turned out, he might well have had a point, because the fireworks were a waste of money. They were mainly duds, and the few that did work were like "flaky Christians!" You know, all fizz and pop but not much else to see! They're just not like I remember when I was small. Firework manufacturers should be more honest with the names. Instead of a roman candle, we had a **roman swindle**! The catherine wheel was a **catherine steal**, and the rocket was more of a **racket**! It was a disaster. And poor Tony and I had the responsibility of igniting these 'wonders'! Well Lord, there was more gunpowder in my son's cap gun than in the whole box of these pyrotechnics!

The party was held at Tudor Toffee's house. He has a big field out the back which is ideal. A stand was set up for the "display" but one after another, the fireworks didn't work, and we were having trouble getting the bonfire to light. Tony threw a dud roman swindle, sorry, candle onto the

paraffin soaked heap, and turned to assist me in the next disappointment. Suddenly, there was a shrill scream, followed by a pop, and a bright blue ball flew into the air, closely tailed by a green one! It was the dud! It had obviously been smouldering and now decided to go off. As soon as the balls hit the bonfire, it burst into flames, sending
the assembled crowd fleeing for their lives, running faster than you can say "Let us take up the offering!"

We kept the biggest rocket until last. As it was too large to balance in a milk bottle, we decided to launch it like a mortar. Tony held a length of plastic pipe against the earth and pointed it sky-wards. I positioned the rocket just inside the mouth of the pipe. We called on everyone's attention for our finale'. I lit the touchpaper and dropped it down the pipe. Tony braced himself. The crowd held its breath. The rocket fizzed into life, and then..! Unfortunately, the ground was very muddy and the rocket embedded itself into the earth, thus refusing to fly. But the sparks shot out from around the bottom of the pipe and scorched all the polish from Tony's shoes. I laughed so much that I fell over the firework stand. What a shambles!

But the night wasn't a total flop, Lord, because I learnt something. One firework did work very well. It was a cascade of sparks called "The Silver Fountain!" The light from that thing was tremendous and it lit up the field, dazzling us all and sending our shadows dancing wildly across the ground. I was amazed at how much brilliance came from such a small object. And it made me think! You have called us to be "a light in darkness!" And there are times when I've felt small and inadequate. But if the gunpowder in the "silver fountain" can temporarily turn night to day, how much more can the Spirit in me make me shine like the sun where there is no light! I will be a light in darkness, Lord, with your help.
Shine Jesus shine, fill this land with the Father's glory!
                          Amen.

DEAR LORD...
THE GREATEST GIFT

Dear Lord,
"Christmas is a-coming and I think I'm getting fat! My trousers are a-bursting and I've grown out of my hat!" I love Christmas, Lord. What a wonderful time! It's the only time when I really enjoy "religious tradition!" The carols are always top of the pops; there's excitement in the air, with the giving and receiving of gifts. But lately, I've been thinking about gifts. Wouldn't it be terrible if we were given a present that was either no use or we didn't know what to do with it. I know it's the thought that counts but when I was a kid, someone always gave me Hi-Karate after shave or cuff-links! Not much use for a nine year old and not much thought either! I didn't know what to do with any of them!

The greatest gift that You gave to Man was "Woman". (Some would debate that statement, but not me!) First You made Adam, then Eve. Then You introduced them to each other and instructed them to "get on with it!" meaning life together.

Now there's a thought! If You weren't around at the beginning of creation, How would Adam know what Eve was, let alone what to do with her. After all, he'd never seen a woman before! If the attraction was purely because she was a creature of similar build and shape, how come he wasn't chatting up Glenys the Gorilla? The whole of creation from that point on would have been a totally different story! An extract from the book of Terrance, "And the serpent hung down from the tree of the knowledge of good and evil, and beckoning Adam, he said, 'I don't like the look of yours!'"

Obviously Lord, You instructed Adam, created Eve, and orchestrated the whole thing! You placed it in our nature to only mate with human beings and no other. It can only be Your doing! There's one in the eye for the evolutionists! Thanks to You, Adam knew what to do with the gift of woman.

It just makes me sad that the world doesn't know what to do with the greatest gift that you gave Mankind, that is Your Son, Jesus! And it becomes even more obvious at Christmas. Christmas to many has become a time of pressure not peace, gain not goodness, hassle not happiness, concern instead of contentment! Jesus doesn't get a look in! To many, He's the last parcel under the tree that nobody wants, and yet He is <u>The</u> greatest gift! I'm starting to feel the sadness of Your heart for the lost! They don't know the importance of Your Son. I'm fed up of seeing "Merry Xmas" instead of "Christmas!" In the past, if people couldn't write, they signed their name with an "X". Or, if someone wanted to remain anonymous, they would be referred to as "Mr X". Neither of these apply to Jesus, but the world doesn't know what He's about! So Lord, it's up to us to tell them!

Christmas without Christ is like breakfast without the grub! It's meaningless! (Do they eat anything at business breakfasts? If not, they're not breaking fast, are they?)

I thank you that it's Christmas, Lord, and I thank you that the fellowship to whom I belong are committed to ensuring that as many people as possible know the significance of that gift under the tree.
Thank you for your greatest gift to us.
Amen.

DEAR LORD...
A NEW CREATION

Dear Lord,

Another year! I can see us all riding on the spaceship called Earth, travelling down deep, dark corridors of space called years. And on every December 31st at precisely 11.59pm and 59 seconds, the whole ship turns down an unknown corridor. Ahead is dark and unexplored; behind is brightly lit and everything seen. It's just the dramatic in me, I suppose. It's a pity we can't warp forward to the summer and leave the winter rain behind, but then we'd miss plenty of planets (or experiences) on the way if we did that. No, let's live every minute.

I wouldn't mind reliving the last new year's eve party, Lord. What a revelation! I bumped into a group of people that I was at school with. And do you know, even though most of them looked different, on talking to them, nothing's really changed! They still have the same old quirks and funny ways. One thing I did learn, Lord, was how my perception of beauty was severely flawed in school. Sharon and Wendy were there! Now at school, these two were some lookers, Father, I can tell you! And I never had the chance to get to know them properly. So I just fancied from afar. But now I wondered what I saw in them in the looks department. I'm no oil painting (except something by Salvador Dali) but I don't think I've changed that much. These two, however, have found time to be very unkind where ageing is concerned. Then a third girl said hello. It was Mandy! Hubba! Hubba! She looked stonking, and yet in school, nobody gave her a second glance. This was a classic case of the ugly duckling. She had matured into a real beauty. And doesn't that happen to your people, Lord? When we gave our lives to you, we became new creations, untainted in your eyes by our past. You saw us as we would become. And as we mature, we become the objects of beauty that you saw at the beginning.

I thank you for creating me again in your likeness. I thank you for the new year, and for the opportunity to become a new man.

Happy new year, Father.

MOORLEY'S

are growing Publishers, adding several new titles to our list each year. We also undertake private publications and commissioned works.

Our range of publications includes: **Books of Verse**
Devotional Poetry
Recitations
Drama
Bible Plays
Sketches
Nativity Plays
Passiontide Plays
Easter Plays
Demonstrations
Resource Books
Assembly Material
Songs & Musicals
Children's Addresses
Prayers & Graces
Daily Readings
Books for Speakers
Activity Books
Quizzes
Puzzles
Painting Books
Daily Readings
Church Stationery
Notice Books
Cradle Rolls
Hymn Board Numbers

Please send a S.A.E. (approx 9" x 6") for the current catalogue or consult your local Christian Bookshop who should stock or be able to order our titles.